A PERFECT DAY FOR GOLF

ISBN 9798408724772

For Our Dad, Mark, who inspires us to embrace every day with joy.

A portion of all book sales will directly support families staying at a Ronald McDonald House in Orlando, FL.

Hello little golfers! There's a lot to learn from the game of golf! Can you help spot the **10 KEY WORDS** our animal friends will encounter during their round?

Responsibility
Accountability
Focus
Respect
Patience
Mindfulness
Kindness
Faith
Composure
Teamwork

Early morning as the day starts,
all animals meet at the golf carts.

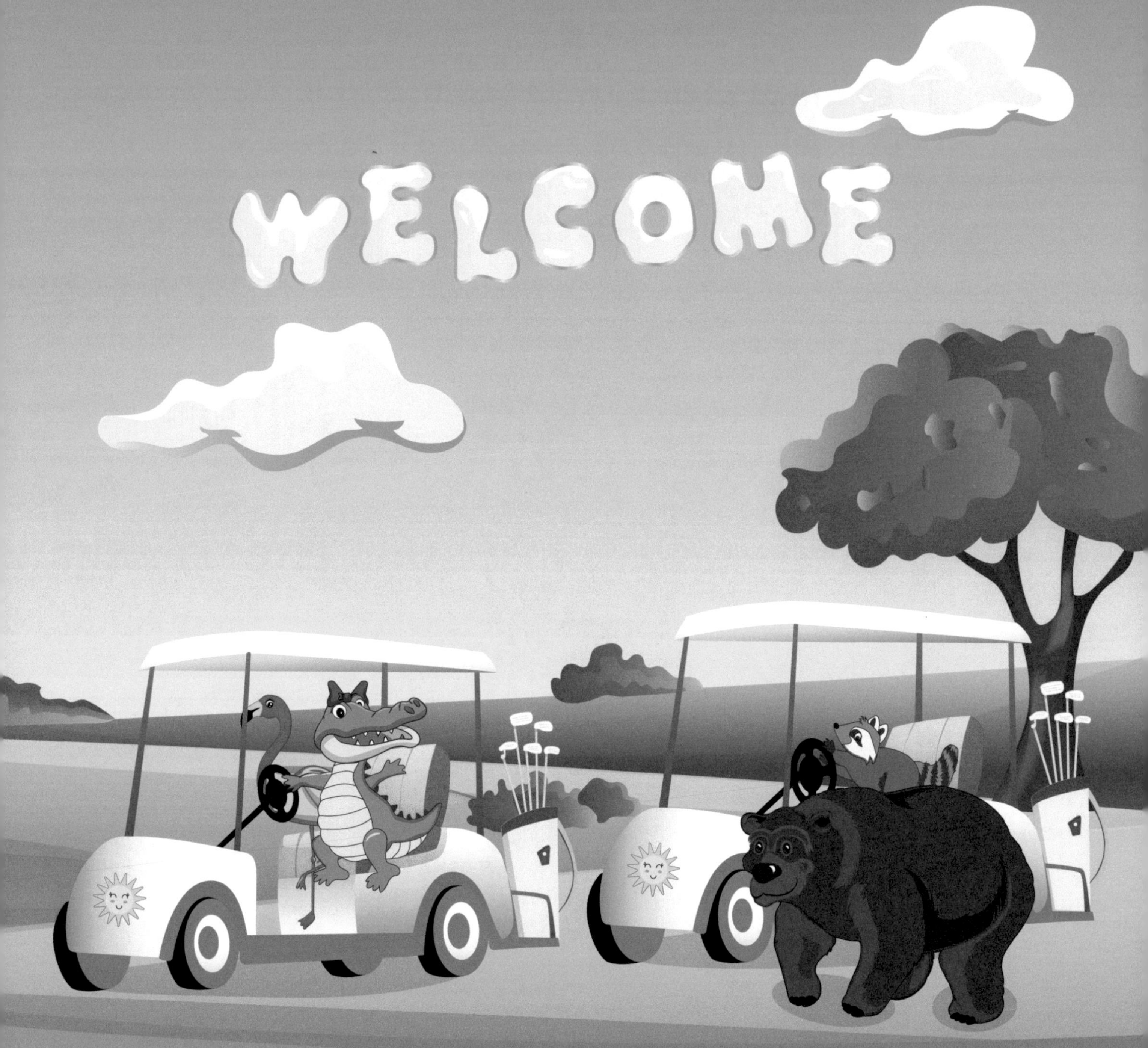
WELCOME

They make their way to the first tee,
where Riley raises the flag for all to see.

Being **responsible** for the home we share, means keeping it tidy and showing we care.

On hole number 2 Gabby sets up her tee.
She swings and hits farther than anyone can see.

She searches everywhere, high and low.
"Where oh where did my ball go?"

Let's check the rules. They'll help guide us through. They make us take accountability for what we do.

RULES

If you lose a ball, you've got a second try. Set up in the same place and watch your ball fly!

Sandra **focuses** and putts, but it goes past the hole.

If we find someone's belongings we treat them with respect. Let's turn them in and do what's correct.

Mindful of his surroundings, Felix notices a lake. This helps him decide which club he should take.

A duck family crosses. Felix waves hello.
Let's all be **kind** wherever we go.

"I'm here in three shots, but the hole still looks far."

"Have **faith** in yourself and you might make a par."

Believe in yourself

composure

Paul's ball takes a bounce–not what he expected.
"I'll keep my **composure**. My game won't be affected."

teamwork

19

Great game everyone! We've finished our round.
Golf is a sport where good values are found.

THE END

What does it mean...

Responsibility is taking care of something and making good decisions.

Accountability is accepting what happens when you do or say something.

Focus is paying close attention to what you are doing.

Respect is treating someone or something well.

Patience is staying calm when you want something to happen before it actually does.

Mindfulness is when you are paying attention to what's around you. It is also when you notice how someone is feeling or behaving.

Kindness is when you are friendly and helpful.

Faith is when you believe in yourself and try something you think you might not be able to do.

Composure is helping yourself calm down when something upsets you.

Teamwork is when friends help each other and work together.

Made in United States
Troutdale, OR
12/19/2023